Specimen Sight-Reading Tests for Organ

including specimen transposition tests

Grades 2–8

The Associated Board of
the Royal Schools of Music

1

suggested registration: **Pr. (Open Diap.) 8' 4' 2'**

Lively and detached (well articulated)

Manual only

2

suggested registration: **Fl. 8'**

Adagio

Manual only

3

suggested registration: **Fl. 8' Pr. (Open Diap.) 4'**

Moderato

Manual only

   AB 2544

4

suggested registration: **Fl. 8'**

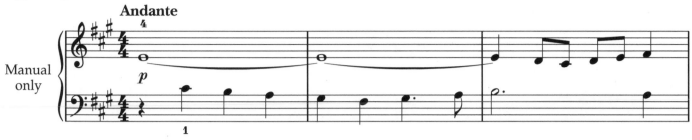

5

suggested registration: **Pr. (Open Diap.) 8' 4'**

6

suggested registration: **Pr. (Open Diap.) 8' 4' 2'**

GRADE 3

1

suggested registration: **Fl. 8' Pr. (Open Diap.) 4'**

2

suggested registration: **Pr. (Open Diap.) 8'**

3

suggested registration: **Pr. (Open Diap.) 8' Fl. 8'**

4

suggested registration: **Fl. 8'**

5

suggested registration: **Pr. (Open Diap.) 8' Fl. 8' 4'**

GRADE 4

1

suggested registration: **Gt. Fl. 8'**
Sw. Fl. 8' Pr. (Open Diap.) 4' box open
Ped. 16'
Sw. to Gt.
Gt. and Sw. to Ped.

2

suggested registration: **Gt. Fl. 8' (4')**
Sw. Fl. 8' 4' box open
Ped. 16'
Sw. to Gt.
Gt. and Sw. to Ped.

1

suggested registration: **Gt. Pr. (Open Diap.) 8' 4' (2')**
Sw. Pr. (Open Diap.) 8' 4' (2') box open
Ped. Pr. (Open Diap.) 16' (8' 4')
Sw. to Gt.
Gt. and Sw. to Ped.

2

suggested registration: **Gt. Fl. 8' 4'**
Sw. Fl. 8' Pr. (Open Diap.) 4' box open
Ped. 16' (or 16' 8')
Sw. to Ped.

GRADE 6

1

suggested registration: **Gt. Pr. 8' 4' 2'**
Sw. Pr. 8' 4' 2' box open
Ped. Pr. 16' 8' 4'
Gt. to Ped.

2

suggested registration: **Gt. 8' 4' 2' (Mixt.)**
Sw. 8' 4' box open
Ped. 16' 8' 4' (Mixt.)
Gt. to Ped.

1

suggested registration: Gt. Pr. 8' 4'
Sw. Fl. 8' Pr. 4' box open
Ped. Pr. 16' 8'
Gt. to Ped.

2

suggested registration: **Gt. Fl. 8' 4'**
Sw. Fl. 8' Pr. 4' box open
Ped. 16' 8'
Gt. to Ped.

1

suggested registration: **Manuals equally balanced**
Ped. 16' 8'
no couplers

2

suggested registration: **Gt. warm combination of 8' and 4' stops**
Ped. 16' 8'
Gt. to Ped.

1

2

1

2

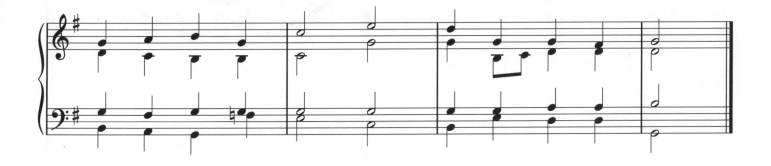

1

2

AB 2544   5/06   Printed by
Halstan & Co. Ltd., Amersham, Bucks., England